Spotlight Solos PLUS

for Late Beginners through Early Intermediates

Music by
Jennifer Eklund

"You are the star, and life is your stage. It's up to you whether or not the audience shouts for an encore."

–Jennifer Eklund

PIANO PRONTO PUBLISHING

PianoPronto.com

Spotlight Solos PLUS

Jennifer Eklund

ISBN 978-1-942751-10-6

Printed in the United States of America

Piano Pronto Publishing, Inc.
PianoPronto.com

Spotlight Solos PLUS

for Late Beginners through Early Intermediates

Music by
Jennifer Eklund

PIANO PRONTO PUBLISHING

PianoPronto.com

1. Out of the Blue

"Opportunities are like sunrises. If you wait too long, you miss them." (William Arthur Ward)

Moderately

Jennifer Eklund

mf

with pedal

mp

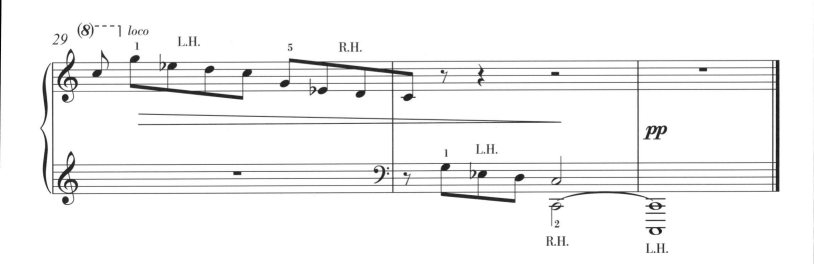

2. It's My Time

"The biggest battles are always right before the sweetest breakthroughs." (Anonymous)

Moderately

Jennifer Eklund

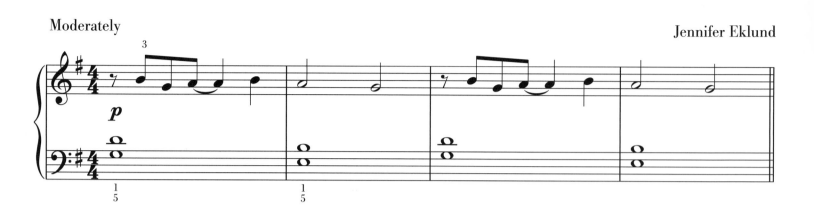

5

3. Above & Beyond

"Don't just meet expectations, exceed them." (Anonymous)

Moderately

Jennifer Eklund

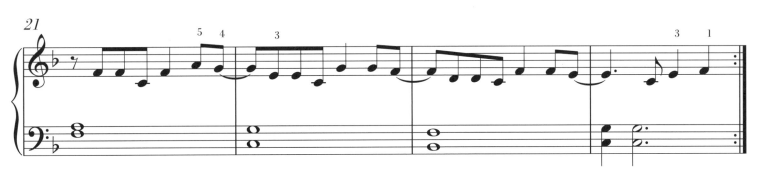

Freely

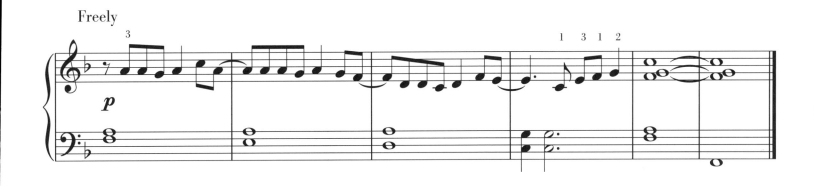

4. Shadowfall

"Never fear shadows. They simply mean there's a light shining nearby." (Ruth E. Renkel)

Mysteriously

Jennifer Eklund

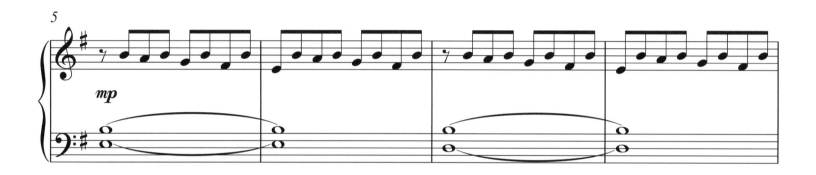

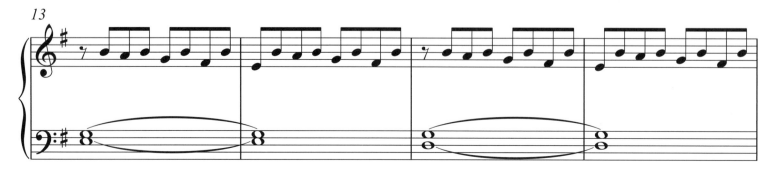

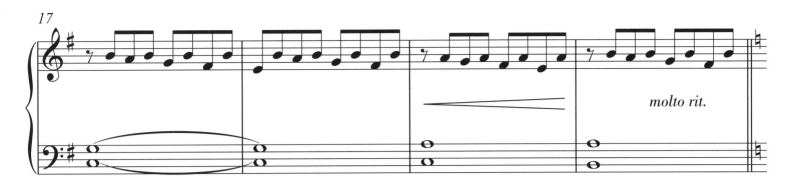

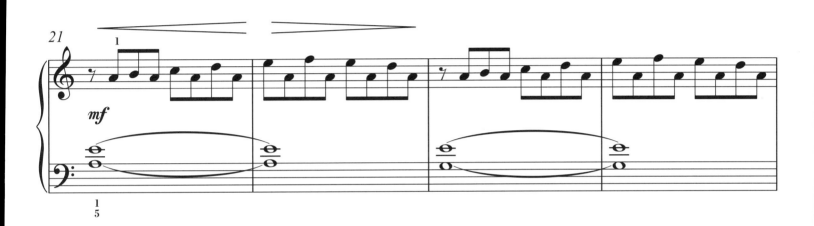

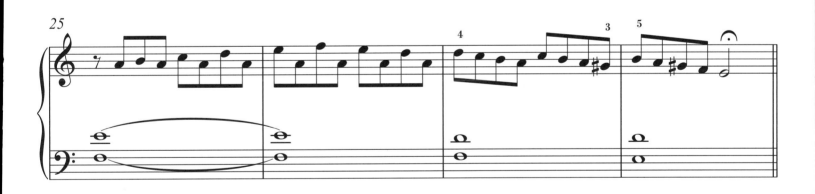

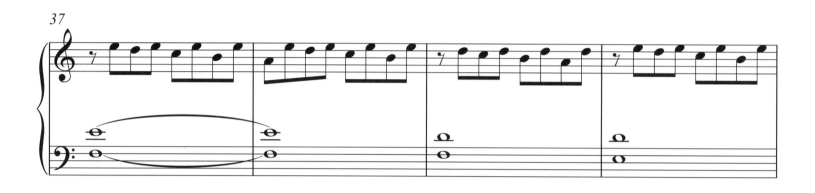

5. Banana Donuts

"When you find your rhythm, march to the beat of your own drum." (Anonymous)

Lively & light

Jennifer Eklund

11

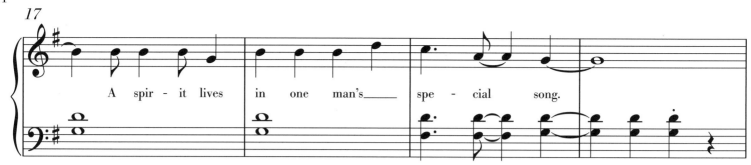

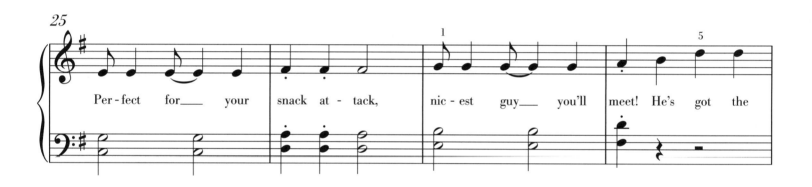

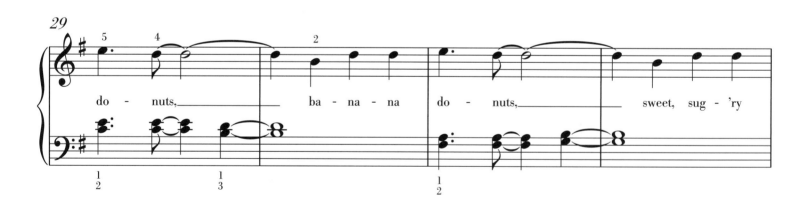

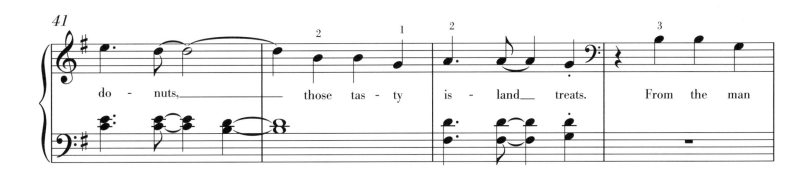

6. Scenic Route

"No road is long with good company." (Turkish Proverb)

Jennifer Eklund

Moderately slow

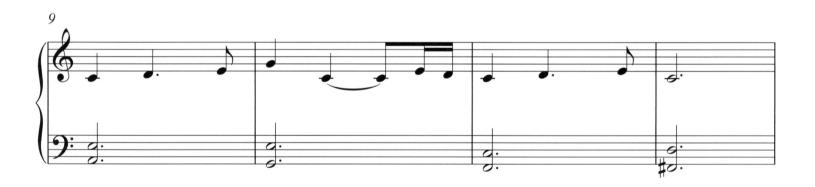

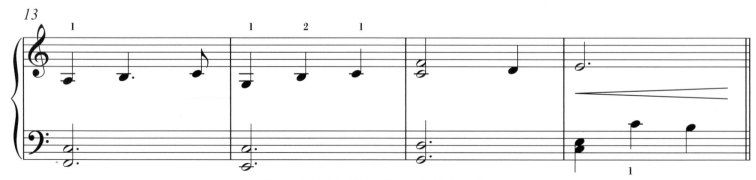

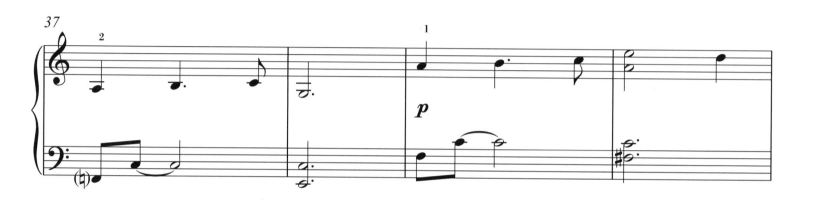

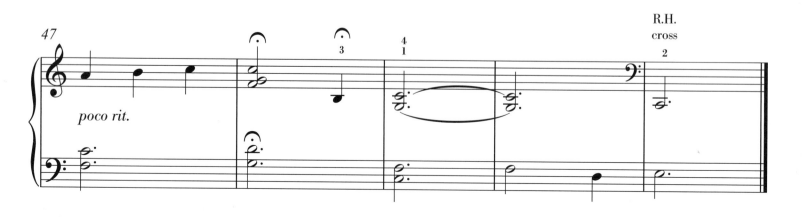

7. Highly Classified

"Be silent if you choose; but when it is necessary, speak—and speak in such a way that people will remember it." (W.A. Mozart)

Jennifer Eklund

Allegro

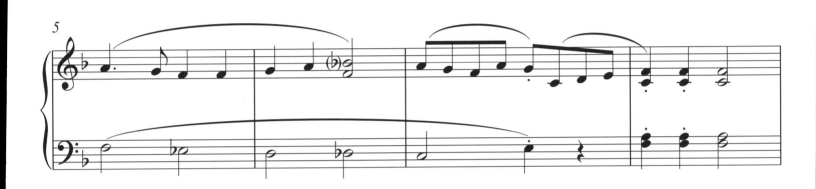

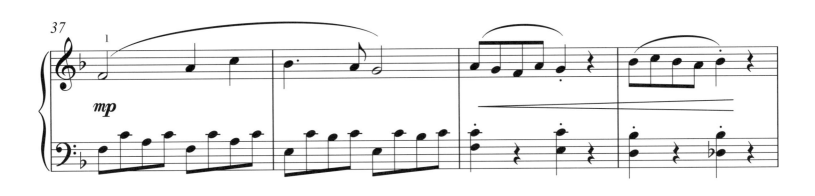

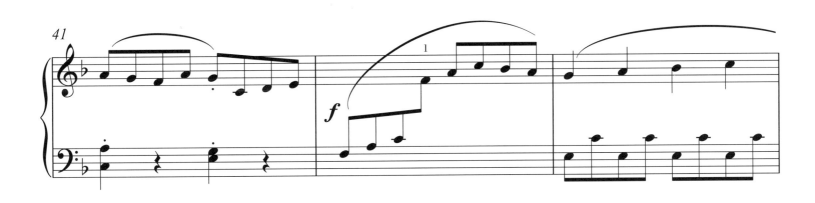

8. Triple Threat

"Work until your idols become your rivals." (Anonymous)

Quickly

Jennifer Eklund

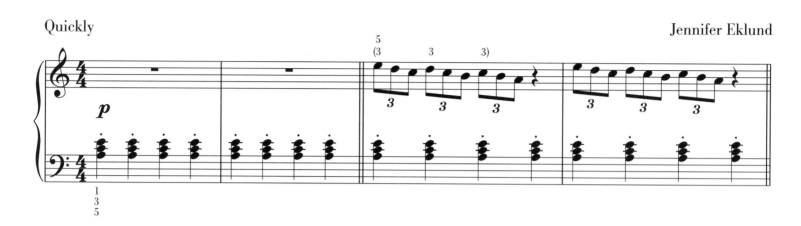

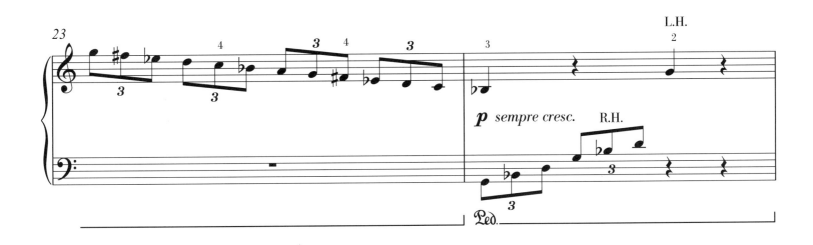

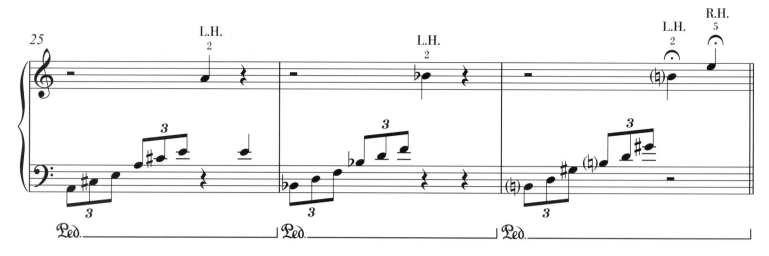

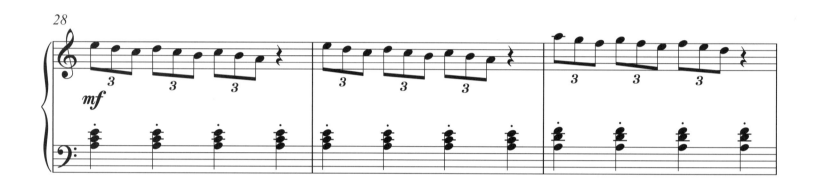

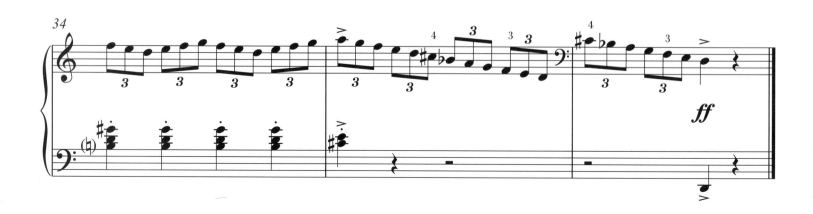

9. Chain Reaction

"Adversity causes some to break, and others to break records." (William Arthur Ward)

Jennifer Eklund

Moderately fast

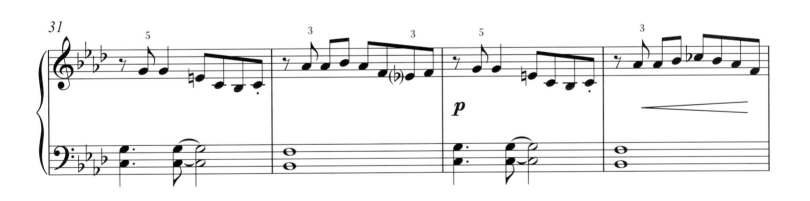

10. Midnight Waltz

"Midnight—strange mystic hour, when the veil between the frail present and the eternal future grows thin." (Harriet Beecher Stowe)

Gently in 1

Jennifer Eklund

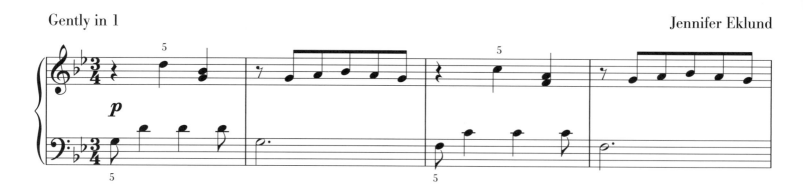

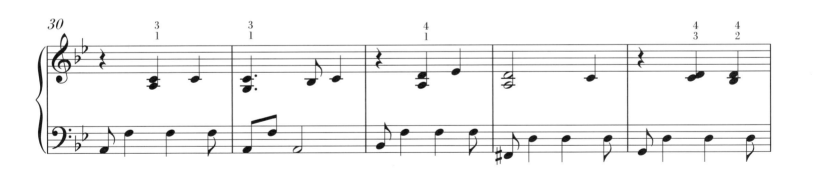

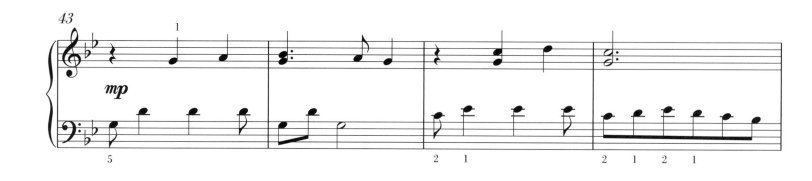

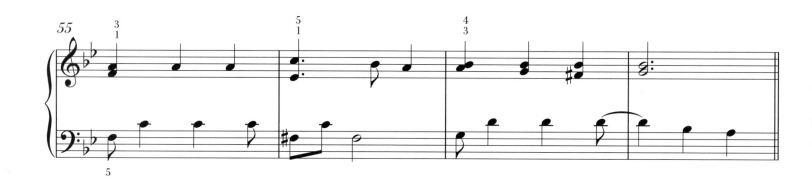

"Work hard. Dream big."